Specific Skill Series

Getting the Facts

Richard A. Boning

Fifth Edition

SRA/McGraw-Hill

Columbus, Ohio

Cover, Back Cover, Kennan Ward/The Stock Market

SRA/McGraw-Hill

A Division of The **McGraw·Hill** *Companies*

Printed in the United States of America.

Send all inquiries to:
    SRA/McGraw-Hill
    8787 Orion Place
    Columbus, OH 43240-4027

ISBN 0-02-687968-9

6 IPC 02 01

To the Teacher

PURPOSE:

GETTING THE FACTS is designed to develop skill in recalling factual information from a single reading. The material is structured so that there is no "turning back" for the answer. The story is on one side; the questions are on the reverse. Readers must take as much as they can from one reading. The knowledge that they cannot turn back to the story helps them gain skill in GETTING THE FACTS.

FOR WHOM:

The skill of GETTING THE FACTS is developed through a series of books spanning ten levels (Picture, Preparatory, A, B, C, D, E, F, G, H). The Picture Level is for pupils who have not acquired a basic sight vocabulary. The Preparatory Level is for pupils who have a basic sight vocabulary but are not quite ready for the first-grade-level book. Books A through H are appropriate for pupils who can read on levels one through eight, respectively. **The use of the *Specific Skill Series Placement Test* is recommended to determine the appropriate level.**

THE NEW EDITION:

The fifth edition of the *Specific Skill Series* maintains the quality and focus that has distinguished this program for more than 25 years. A key element central to the program's success has been the unique nature of the reading selections. Nonfiction pieces about current topics have been designed to stimulate the interest of students, motivating them to use the comprehension strategies they have learned to further their reading. To keep this important aspect of the program intact, a percentage of the reading selections have been replaced in order to ensure the continued relevance of the subject material.

In addition, a significant percentage of the artwork in the program has been replaced to give the books a contemporary look. The cover photographs are designed to appeal to readers of all ages.

SESSIONS:

Short practice sessions are the most effective. It is desirable to have a practice session every day or every other day, using a few units each session.

To the Teacher

SCORING:

Pupils should record their answers on the reproducible worksheets. The worksheets make scoring easier and provide uniform records of the pupils' work. Using worksheets also avoids consuming the exercise books.

It is important for pupils to know how well they are doing. For this reason, units should be scored as soon as they have been completed. Then a discussion can be held in which pupils justify their choices. (The Integrated Language Activities, many of which are open-ended, do not lend themselves to an objective score; thus there are no answer keys for these pages.)

GENERAL INFORMATION ON *GETTING THE FACTS*:

GETTING THE FACTS varies in content. It contains stories about mysteries and unexplained happenings, remarkable people, and odd customs. It was the author's intention to include stories that would help stretch the imagination, spark new hobbies, promote admiration for outstanding achievements, and develop a sense of wonder about our world. Interest ratings were obtained from junior and senior high students as well as elementary school pupils. The stories included in GETTING THE FACTS are those to which the readers reacted most strongly.

There is only one correct answer for each question. The incorrect answers may very well be true and make sense. The readers may know that they are true from their own experiences. The only correct answer choice, however, is the one that is stated in the story. GETTING THE FACTS means getting the facts from a particular story. It really means knowing whether or not something was stated. This must be made clear to pupils.

SUGGESTED STEPS:

1. Pupils read the story. (In the Picture Level books, the pupils look at the pictures.)
2. After completing the story, pupils turn to the questions on the reverse side and choose the letters of the correct answers.
3. Pupils write the letters of the correct answers on the worksheets.
4. Pupils may return to the story only after their answers have been recorded and scored.

RELATED MATERIALS:

Specific Skill Series Placement Tests, which enable the teacher to place pupils at their appropriate levels in each skill, are available for the Elementary (Pre-1–6) and Midway (4–8) grade levels.

About This Book

A **fact** is something that can be proven true. It is something that can be checked. These statements are facts.

- Dairy products are naturally high in sodium.
- All of Asia lies west of the International Date Line.
- Andrew Jackson was President of the United States from 1829 to 1837.

There are facts in everything you read. Read this paragraph:

There are about 240 different kinds of turtles. One thing they all have in common is a shell that covers most of the body. The shell serves as a suit of armor, protecting the turtle from its enemies. Turtles range in size from the gigantic leatherback turtle, which may grow to eight feet in length, to the common mud turtle, which measures only three to five inches in length.

These are some facts from the paragraph:

- There are about 240 kinds of turtles.
- All turtles have a shell.
- The shell protects the turtle from enemies.
- The leatherback turtle is the largest turtle; it may grow to eight feet in length.
- The mud turtle is the smallest turtle; it measures three to five inches in length.

Articles that are written to present facts are called nonfiction. A nonfiction article must generally be read differently from a story that you read just for fun. You should read more slowly when you are reading to find out new information. To understand the information, you may need to figure out the meanings of unfamiliar words. To remember the facts, you may need to reread part of the article.

In this book you will read nonfiction articles on many different subjects. After you have read an article, turn the page to find ten questions about it. The correct answers to the questions are facts from the article. There is only one correct answer for each question. The incorrect answers may be true and make sense, but the only correct answer choice is the one that is stated in the article. "Getting the Facts" means getting the facts from a particular article. Only by reading the article carefully can you answer the questions correctly.

CONTENTS

UNIT 1
Ho Hum

What do you do when you are tired or bored? Do you stare out the window? Do you take a nap? Does your mind wander a bit? Chances are you do one of these things or something similar. However, one thing that almost everyone does when tired or bored is to yawn.

When you're tired or bored, your body usually feels a little draggy. You yawn, quite simply, to bring more oxygen into your body. The extra oxygen makes you more alert. If you stifle a yawn—you know, keep your mouth closed so you can't yawn—you don't get the extra dose of oxygen your body needs. You yawn again and again—and maybe even again.

We know now that yawns are good for you, but people haven't always known that. People in ancient times thought that valuable life spirits escaped the body in a yawn. Some people even thought that yawning meant breathing out one's last breath.

Out of these fears came three customs many of us carry on today. Long ago, when feeling a yawn coming on, people turned their heads and covered their mouths. When the yawn was over they apologized for yawning. Why? People covered their mouths to, literally, "save" their lives. They turned their heads so others wouldn't see them yawn. They apologized for yawning because they knew, as we know, just how contagious a yawn can be. Who wanted to feel responsible for causing someone else to lose his or her life?

Therefore, the next time the urge hits you, open up your mouth and give a great big yawn. Pull that oxygen deep inside, and enjoy every moment of it. Ancient people were right: yawns *do* contain a breath of life. They just had it backwards.

We came a long way when we discovered why we yawn, but we still don't know why yawns are so catching. That's one question that medical scientists have yet to answer. When we see someone else yawn, the yawn message goes right to our own yawn headquarters, and we yawn. Maybe our Yawn Commander thinks that things have been a little slow and that a dose of oxygen just might liven things up.

It sounds like a good idea. Ho hum. Pass it on.

1. People yawn when they are—
   - **(A) excited or happy**
   - **(B) tired or happy**
   - **(C) tired or bored**
   - **(D) sleepy or excited**

2. You yawn to—
   - **(A) stay awake**
   - **(B) bring more oxygen in**
   - **(C) keep from laughing**
   - **(D) let oxygen out**

3. Extra oxygen makes you more—
   - **(A) tired**
   - **(B) bored**
   - **(C) alert**
   - **(D) awake**

4. Yawning is—
   - **(A) good for you**
   - **(B) scary**
   - **(C) dangerous**
   - **(D) a nuisance**

5. Ancient people thought yawns released—
   - **(A) evil spirits**
   - **(B) oxygen**
   - **(C) germs**
   - **(D) valuable life forces**

6. Ancient fears gave us—
   - **(A) new knowledge**
   - **(B) three customs**
   - **(C) new fears**
   - **(D) several laws**

7. Long ago, after a yawn, people—
   - **(A) apologized**
   - **(B) lost their lives**
   - **(C) laughed**
   - **(D) lost oxygen**

8. People covered their mouths to—
   - **(A) chew secretly**
   - **(B) hide their tongues**
   - **(C) "save" their lives**
   - **(D) use their hands**

9. We know, as ancient people did, that—
   - **(A) yawns are dangerous**
   - **(B) babies yawn a lot**
   - **(C) yawns are fun**
   - **(D) yawns are contagious**

10. Why yawns are contagious is a question to be answered by—
    - **(A) our Yawn Commander**
    - **(B) everyone**
    - **(C) medical scientists**
    - **(D) ancient people**

UNIT 2
A Canine Question

Did dogs learn to bark from humans? The question suggests funny images of a human on all fours barking at a dog and the dog barking back. Yet there is evidence that before the dog was domesticated, it couldn't or didn't bark.

The wild Australian dogs called dingoes, for example, do not bark when they grow up in the wilderness. When tamed and made pets, however, they do. Wolves, foxes, wild dogs, and other members of the canine family, in their natural states, howl, growl, whine, or yelp—but do not bark.

Some writers on early America have written that dogs of Native Americans, far less domesticated than European dogs, did not bark. In the New World especially, whole nonbarking breeds were found. Columbus, visiting the island of Santa Marta in 1494, found a small breed of white domesticated dogs that neither barked nor howled. The breed is now extinct.

So common were barkless dogs in the New World that some people believed it was bad air in America that created the problem.

Scientists know that wolves, dingoes, Inuit sled dogs, and other wild canines biologically close to dogs can bark, for when placed in the company of barking dogs, they all soon learn how, and barking becomes a habit to them.

Furthermore, even today on certain islands and in Africa, there are breeds of domesticated dogs that have never learned to bark. These dogs are simply not in contact with other barking animals. Scientists believe that barking is only a capability of canines. Almost all of them can do it, but they must learn it.

From whom did the first domesticated dogs learn to bark? From humans, scientists think. Dogs were tamed by humans. The domesticated environment was much gentler than the wild. Food was easily available, and natural enemies were controlled. The dog no longer needed its natural yelp, howl, and whine to protect and express itself.

People speak; they communicate by sound. Dogs, hearing human speech, may have tried to imitate it and ended up with the bark. After that, one dog taught another.

1. Wild dogs of Australia are called—
   - (A) bingos
   - (B) collies
   - (C) dingoes
   - (D) danes

2. In its wild state, this Australian dog does not—
   - (A) howl
   - (B) bark
   - (C) whine
   - (D) walk

3. On his voyage Columbus visited the island of—
   - (A) Puerto Rico
   - (B) San Juan
   - (C) Bermuda
   - (D) Santa Marta

4. The small breed of white dogs Columbus found is now—
   - (A) popular
   - (B) valuable
   - (C) extinct
   - (D) worthless

5. Most canines have to learn how to—
   - (A) bark
   - (B) whine
   - (C) eat
   - (D) howl

6. Scientists believe dogs were first taught to bark by—
   - (A) other dogs
   - (B) foxes
   - (C) wolves
   - (D) humans

7. The domesticated environment was—
   - (A) wild
   - (B) unfriendly
   - (C) fierce
   - (D) gentler

8. In domesticated surroundings, there was more available—
   - (A) kindness
   - (B) food
   - (C) shelter
   - (D) water

9. The wild dogs howled, whined, and yelped for—
   - (A) enjoyment
   - (B) sorrow
   - (C) perfection
   - (D) protection

10. Barking may be the result of dogs trying to imitate—
    - (A) foxes
    - (B) wolves
    - (C) humans
    - (D) cows

UNIT 3
A Sweet Story

How is your sweet tooth? Does it act up all the time? As you probably know, the expression "a sweet tooth" means one's hunger for sweets. Some people have it, some don't. It's always been that way. In some countries people were eating candy as far back as A.D. 500. In others there was no such thing as candy until the seventeenth century.

Back in A.D. 500 the Persians were making solid sugar from sugar cane. They called their solid sugar food kandi-sefid. The first half of their label remained.

In those days not everyone knew how to make sugar. Yet nearly everyone had a sweet tooth to be satisfied. Instead of sugar, people used honey. From studying the Egyptians we have learned that they had candy recipes whose chief ingredients were dates and honey. They called their candy sweet-meats. In the Far East every community had an official candy-maker who used a mixture of honey, almonds, and figs. Candy recipes were a guarded secret.

Despite its popularity in the East, at that time people of Europe didn't know what candy was. Eating candy for pleasure didn't start in Europe until the 1600s. Before that Europeans had used a sweetened syrup to improve the bitter taste of medicine, but it had never occurred to them to make candy. Then in the 1600s European countries began trading with their colonies in the New World. Suddenly they were importing great amounts of sugar cane. Not until then did candy-making begin. After the French candied fruits, many other recipes followed.

When it came to candy, Americans wasted no time. The colonists discovered early that the native American maple tree oozed a delightfully sweet sap. It didn't take long before maple-tree candy recipes caught on. Taffy was one of the first and one of the most popular. The maple sap was also dried and made into rock candy. Candy shops popped up all over to sell these treats. Today business is still brisk in candy stores that sell every type of candy imaginable.

1. People were eating candy as early as—
    (A) **500 B.C.**   (B) **A.D. 200**
    (C) **A.D. 500**   (D) **150 B.C.**

2. Sugar cane was used by the—
    (A) **Egyptians**   (B) **Pilgrims**
    (C) **Indians**   (D) **Persians**

3. One substitute for sugar was—
    (A) **maple**   (B) **honey**
    (C) **molasses**   (D) **raisins**

4. Dates were used in candy by the—
    (A) **Romans**   (B) **Persians**
    (C) **Egyptians**   (D) **Indians**

5. In the Far East candy-makers used honey, figs, and—
    (A) **chestnuts**   (B) **cashews**
    (C) **peanuts**   (D) **almonds**

6. In Europe candy was first eaten for pleasure in the—
    (A) **1400s**   (B) **1600s**
    (C) **1700s**   (D) **1800s**

7. The Europeans had used syrup to improve the taste of—
    (A) **milk**   (B) **meat**
    (C) **medicine**   (D) **vegetables**

8. One recipe the French used was candied—
    (A) **wheat**   (B) **bread**
    (C) **nuts**   (D) **fruits**

9. Americans discovered sweet sap from the—
    (A) **cherry tree**   (B) **apple tree**
    (C) **maple tree**   (D) **peach tree**

10. This sap was dried and made into—
    (A) **gum**   (B) **rock candy**
    (C) **jelly**   (D) **licorice**

UNIT 4
The Building with a Soul

At the same time as European settlers were first landing in America, India was ruled by a gentle and wise king named Shah Jehan, who lived in the capital city of Agra with his devoted and inspiring queen, Arjemand. From the moment they first met, they had loved each other deeply. Shah Jehan called his empress Mumtaz Mahal, the Chosen of the Palace, and everything he did was for her.

He brought celebrated artists and architects from distant lands to build her the most beautiful marble city in the world. He ruled his people for her, and India became a rich and contented land.

Then Mumtaz Mahal was stricken with a fatal fever, and Shah Jehan watched in anguish as his beautiful wife died. For days afterward the king would not sleep, eat, or speak to anyone. At last he summoned his finest architect, a Persian named Usted Isa, and commanded, "Build a tomb where I may bury her body. Make it as beautiful as she was beautiful. Make it as delicate as she was delicate, make it the image and the soul of her beauty."

Usted Isa set to work, choosing the most fragrant garden in Agra, overlooking the Jumna River. From a white marble base the monument began to take shape, white as ivory, soft and delicate, with slender minarets at each corner and a glorious white dome above its center. Jehan brought sculptors and jewelers from Europe, and he ordered tons of silver from Persia for the massive doors. From Arabia he brought ten thousand pearls to be woven into a canopy over the casket of Arjemand. The king insisted that the Taj Mahal, the Crown of Mahal, must become the one perfect thing in India.

The Taj Mahal stands today, surrounded by gardens, pools, fountains, and trees. Inside, the jeweled caskets of Mumtaz Mahal and Shah Jehan stand side by side.

Because of the love they had for each other, it is said that the Taj Mahal has a soul, and that if two lovers enter the gardens together to watch the full moon rise, they may perhaps see the image of the queen for one magic moment among the moonbeams.

1. Shah Jehan was a ruler of—

    (A) Greece   (B) Turkey

    (C) India   (D) Arabia

2. Arjemand was Shah Jehan's—

    (A) sister   (B) wife

    (C) daughter   (D) mother

3. From distant lands he brought artists and—

    (A) teachers   (B) scientists

    (C) doctors   (D) architects

4. He wanted to build Arjemand a city of—

    (A) pearls   (B) glass

    (C) marble   (D) crystal

5. Mumtaz Mahal became sick with a fatal—

    (A) heart condition   (B) fever

    (C) lung disease   (D) eye disease

6. Finally the Shah had an architect build a—

    (A) park   (B) statue

    (C) library   (D) tomb

7. The doors were made of—

    (A) gold   (B) bronze

    (C) silver   (D) aluminum

8. The canopy was composed of ten thousand—

    (A) emeralds   (B) pearls

    (C) sapphires   (D) diamonds

9. Today the Taj Mahal is surrounded by gardens, fountains, and—

    (A) beaches   (B) parks

    (C) pools   (D) mountains

10. The Taj Mahal is said to have a—

    (A) mind   (B) heart

    (C) witch   (D) soul

UNIT 5
A Better Mousetrap

The American poet Ralph Waldo Emerson is thought to have said that the world will beat a path to the door of a person who can make a better mousetrap than the neighbors can.

How would a "better mousetrap" come to be invented? According to Sir Alexander Fleming, who discovered the "wonder drug" penicillin, "One finds what one is not looking for." Penicillin, like x-rays, electric current, and radioactivity, was an accidental discovery. One better mousetrap was an accidental discovery, too.

What eventually evolved turned out to be even better, or simpler, than the very uncomplex spring mousetrap so readily available. The ordinary spring mousetrap is the one baited with cheese or bread, or even peanut butter—the one that snaps at fingers if the bar isn't hooked just right! How does a mousetrap that has no springs (thus no pinched fingers) and needs no bait sound? It sounds pretty good, doesn't it—especially when you learn that it works on more than one mouse at once.

This magic trap also works on rats, cockroaches, and ants. And it actually doesn't trap them. It repels them.

Bob Brown, the inventor, actually calls his invention a rat repellent box. It works by producing a series of signals that are pitched at a million cycles a second. This sound is much higher than we humans can hear, but the pests can hear it, and it scrambles their senses. The boxes work so well that they have been bought by farmers, universities, and governments. They have been used in chicken houses, grain warehouses, and food stores all over North ·and South America.

How did this discovery happen? Quite by accident.

In 1971 Bob Brown was putting together an electric guitar. He was working in his garage in California. Somehow, quite by accident, he crossed some electrical wires. The resident rats, also "working" in Brown's garage, hurried away from the piercing (for them) noise. Although Brown didn't hear the noise, he heard the rats scrambling for safety. Knowing what must have happened, he put aside his guitar. And the rat repellent box was born.

Having had polio, Bob Brown was, at the time of his discovery, working from a wheelchair. He was unemployed. His invention made him a wealthy man.

UNIT 5
A Better Mousetrap

1. Penicillin was—
   (A) a disease
   (B) a mousetrap
   (C) a kind of peanut butter
   (D) an accidental discovery

2. The new mousetrap—
   (A) repels mice
   (B) kills mice
   (C) eats mice
   (D) discovers mice

3. The rat box was invented by—
   (A) Ralph Waldo Emerson
   (B) Bob Brown
   (C) Sir Alexander Fleming
   (D) the president of a university

4. The rat box produces signals pitched at—
   (A) ten cycles a second
   (B) a hundred cycles a second
   (C) a thousand cycles a second
   (D) a million cycles a second

5. The sound produced by the box scrambles the pests'—
   (A) eggs
   (B) cycles
   (C) senses
   (D) legs

6. Rat boxes have been used all over—
   (A) the world
   (B) North and South America
   (C) the United States
   (D) California

7. The rat box was invented in—
   (A) 1791
   (B) 1917
   (C) 1971
   (D) 1977

8. In 1971 Bob Brown was putting together—
   (A) a garage
   (B) a mousetrap
   (C) an electric guitar
   (D) a sandwich

9. He accidentally crossed some—
   (A) signals
   (B) music tapes
   (C) garden hoses
   (D) electrical wires

10. At the time of his discovery, Bob Brown was—
    (A) a college president
    (B) unemployed
    (C) a millionaire
    (D) a musician

UNIT 6
Feathered but Flightless

No one can forget the sight of a flock of geese flying south for the winter. First there is a loud honking sound. Then the birds draw closer, and the lucky birdwatcher can see the migrating geese overhead in their V formation. It is truly a thrilling sight.

Yet not all birds can soar into the sky. In fact, there are more than forty different kinds of birds that cannot fly. No matter how hard they try, the best these birds can do is to flap their wings and run along the ground. Sometimes they cannot even do that!

Just about everyone has seen a penguin. This humorous little creature likes cool weather, so it makes its home far down in the Southern Hemisphere. And it chooses to live in the seas rather than on dry land. The wings of a penguin are really fast-moving flippers that propel it rapidly through the cold water.

Another well-known non-flying bird is the ostrich. Tipping the scales at a good three hundred pounds and often reaching eight feet in height, it can run as fast as thirty-five miles per hour and use its foot as a weapon. Very often a kick from an ostrich can kill a hungry lion. Ostriches, which live on the plains of Africa, are noted for the beautiful colors of their feathers.

Although most ducks can fly, there are three species that cannot. For some reason these birds have developed shorter wings than their flying cousins. They can only splash above or swim beneath the surface of the water. Sometimes they are called steamer ducks because they use their wings like the paddle wheels on an old-fashioned steamboat.

Other birds unable to fly include the emu, the rhea, the dodo (now extinct), and the cassowary, a native of New Guinea. Most of these birds are harmless, but if you see a cassowary kicking out with its knife-sharp claws, run for cover. Persons have been seriously injured and even killed by this flightless but dangerous bird!

UNIT 6
Feathered but Flightless

1. The number of birds that cannot fly amounts to—
   - (A) over sixty
   - (C) over ninety
   - (B) less than forty
   - (D) over forty

2. A bird that lives in a cool climate and likes the sea is the—
   - (A) robin
   - (C) penguin
   - (B) ostrich
   - (D) eagle

3. The ostrich weighs over—
   - (A) 300 ounces
   - (C) 30 pounds
   - (B) 300 pounds
   - (D) 800 pounds

4. As a weapon, the ostrich uses its—
   - (A) foot
   - (C) beak
   - (B) tail
   - (D) wings

5. Using this weapon, the ostrich has been known to kill a—
   - (A) lion
   - (C) tiger
   - (B) bear
   - (D) wolf

6. Some ducks cannot fly because they have—
   - (A) longer wings
   - (C) shorter legs
   - (B) heavier feathers
   - (D) shorter wings

7. Ducks that use their wings like paddles are known as—
   - (A) streamers
   - (C) steamers
   - (B) rovers
   - (D) sailors

8. Another bird that cannot fly is the—
   - (A) parrot
   - (C) swallow
   - (B) buzzard
   - (D) emu

9. A native bird of New Guinea is the—
   - (A) emu
   - (C) crow
   - (B) cassowary
   - (D) castaway

10. This New Guinea bird has razor-sharp—
    - (A) teeth
    - (C) wings
    - (B) feathers
    - (D) claws

Did you know that much of the wildlife we are familiar with is relatively new? This is true when we think not only of the age of our planet, but also of how long ago some prehistoric animals, such as the dinosaurs, became extinct. We know a little about some of these early giant reptiles (even though they died out more than 65 million years ago), but not a lot. Such animals as mammoths, mastodons, saber-toothed tigers, and giant sloths roamed the land many thousands of years ago, but they gradually died out. One creature that became extinct fairly recently is the dodo, whom you met briefly in "Feathered but Flightless." Read the following paragraphs about the dodo.

Relatively speaking, the dodo became extinct not so very long ago—probably in the early 1680s. This unusual bird lived on the island of Mauritius (say "mo RISH us"), located in the southwestern part of the Indian Ocean. In its island habitat, the dodo had no predators. Therefore, because it rarely had to fly to escape enemies, it gradually lost the use of its wings. The dodo, which looked something like a turkey, had very small wings, short legs, and a stout, roundish body. Its bill was large and thick, with a hook at the end. Adult dodos weighed about fifty pounds.

The Portuguese sailors who first explored the island hunted dodos for food. Because dodos moved slowly and did not fly, they were easily captured. (Reportedly, the meat of a dodo was tough and stringy, and didn't improve with long, slow cooking.) The dodo might have had a chance but for the Dutch who settled on Mauritius in the 1640s, bringing their dogs, cats, and hogs with them. These domestic animals found the dodo and its eggs easy prey. Forty years later, the dodo had become extinct.

A. Exercising Your Skill

What do you know about extinct animals such as the dodo? Make two lists. In one list, write facts about what caused the dodo to become extinct. In the other list, write the names of other animals you know of that are now extinct. Share your lists with your classmates.

B. Expanding Your Skill

The dodo has been extinct for over three hundred years now. Other birds and animals, still alive, are in danger of becoming extinct. What are the common threats today to such creatures as the panda, the humpback whale, the snow leopard, and the whooping crane? Overhunting or overfishing are examples of ways in which some species of wildlife are threatened. Find out facts about other ways in which wildlife is threatened, and list a few of these facts. Some of these facts may relate to what has been happening in or near wilderness areas or natural habitats. Compare your list with your classmates' lists.

C. Exploring Language

The following chart organizes facts that relate to the welfare of wildlife by topic. First, read the chart. Then choose one of the topics—*Threats to Wildlife* or *Protection of Wildlife*—and write a paragraph. Besides drawing upon the facts listed to develop complete sentences for your paragraph, also draw upon what you know from your own experience or reading.

Threats to Wildlife	Protection of Wildlife
1. overhunting and overfishing	1. zoos and wildlife parks
2. water pollution	2. conservation of wilderness areas
3. air pollution	3. protection of wetlands and forests
4. uses of harmful pesticides	4. stricter laws limiting hunting and fishing
5. overdevelopment of wilderness areas	5. environmental measures to clean up air and water
6. cutting down forests	

D. Expressing Yourself

Choose one of these activities.

1. Both the whooping crane and the peregrine falcon are large, beautiful North American birds that were once in great danger of becoming extinct. They're not "out of the woods" yet! However, their future does look brighter. Find out what has been done to help these two species of birds. How have the whooping crane and the peregrine falcon, and their habitats, been protected? What else have naturalists done to ensure the future of these birds? What facts can you find out?

2. "Dead as a dodo" is an idiom with a fairly clear meaning. What other idioms, old sayings, or figures of speech do you know that contain a reference to birds? What do they mean? Do their meanings as figures of speech have any basis in fact, as "dead as a dodo" does?

3. Fact: Birds developed with wings so that they could more easily find food. Fact: Wings also provide a means of defense for birds, such as escaping from enemies or scaring predators away from nests. How do birds that cannot fly escape danger? Ostriches have long legs and can run very fast. The cassowary has sharp claws. How do the emu and the rhea defend themselves? And what facts can you discover about birds' enemies? Who are they? From the time an egg is laid, what is the greatest threat to a bird?

UNIT 7
The Channel Conqueror

In 1922 Gertrude Ederle was a fifteen-year-old with dimples and long, long curls. She lived with her parents above the family butcher shop. Gertrude wanted to get her hair cut, but her mother would not permit it.

Mrs. Ederle told Gertrude that if she entered every swimming contest in the area, she could have her hair bobbed. Gertrude was a good swimmer, but her mother thought it would be impossible for Gertrude to attend every meet.

But Ederle liked swimming enough to miss none of the competitions. The more she swam, the faster she got. While performing in the International Cup Race with fifty-two entrants, Ederle glanced back and saw that nobody was even close. After winning that race, she had her hair bobbed.

Ederle went on to win the Battery to Sandy Hook Race across New York Harbor in a record seven hours, eleven minutes. Was she ready to try swimming across the English Channel? No woman had ever tried it. A Captain Webb had breast-stroked across the Channel in 1875, but, since then, seventy men had failed.

The water in the Channel is warm enough for swimming only during July, August, and September. Even then, the twenty-one mile stretch between England and France is rough and cold. Storms in the Channel are so sudden that fifteen-foot waves often seem to appear out of nowhere.

On her first try Ederle failed because companions on the boat accompanying her mistakenly judged her to be unconscious and pulled her out.

Bitterly disappointed, she got a new coach and went to Cap Gris Nez, France, to train. Her sister Margaret went along and helped Ederle design a lighter, two-piece bathing suit for racing.

In 1926 Ederle was ready to try the Channel again. If she succeeded in swimming the Channel this time, the *New York Daily News* would reward her with a red sports car. She was nine miles out when sudden strong winds brought rain and heavy swells. She battled on. It took her four hours to go only three miles. The sea was so wild that her coach ordered her out. Gertrude Ederle said, "What for?"

After fourteen hours and thirty-one minutes of swimming, the nineteen-year-old pulled wearily up on the English shore. Not only was she the first woman to swim the Channel, but she had broken the record for the Channel swim that had been set earlier by a man. And she got the red car!

1. Gertrude Ederle was—
   - (A) fifteen in 1926
   - (B) twenty-two in 1915
   - (C) nineteen in 1922
   - (D) fifteen in 1922

2. At that time Ederle's goal was to—
   - (A) get a car
   - (B) swim the Channel
   - (C) cut her hair
   - (D) tour France

3. Young Gertrude got what she wanted by—
   - (A) letting her hair grow
   - (B) entering every swimming meet
   - (C) going to France
   - (D) setting a record

4. On her first try to swim the Channel, Ederle was—
   - (A) left on shore
   - (B) made a lifeguard
   - (C) rewarded with a car
   - (D) pulled out

5. With her new coach Ederle went to train in—
   - (A) England
   - (B) Ireland
   - (C) France
   - (D) New York

6. Gertrude Ederle's sister helped design a new—
   - (A) lifeboat
   - (B) bathing suit
   - (C) racing car
   - (D) hairstyle

7. On her second try to swim the Channel, Ederle battled—
   - (A) whales and sharks
   - (B) low tides
   - (C) bitter disappointment
   - (D) winds and rain

8. It took Ederle four hours to go—
   - (A) one and one-half miles
   - (B) fourteen miles
   - (C) three miles
   - (D) across the Channel

9. When she successfully swam the Channel, Ederle was—
   - (A) fifteen
   - (B) thirty-one
   - (C) twenty-two
   - (D) nineteen

10. Before Ederle succeeded in swimming the Channel,—
    - (A) no men had succeeded
    - (B) no women had succeeded
    - (C) seventy men had succeeded
    - (D) one woman had succeeded

UNIT 8
The Real First President

If you ask almost anybody who the first President of the United States was, the answer you'll get is George Washington. If you ask somebody from Maryland, though, you might get a different answer: John Hanson.

There really was a John Hanson. There is a statue of him in the rotunda of the Capitol in Washington, D.C.; there is a John Hanson Highway connecting Washington with Annapolis, Maryland; and there is the town of Hanson, Maryland.

In 1781, after Maryland had become the last of the thirteen colonies to ratify the Articles of Confederation, the continental Congress unanimously elected John Hanson of Maryland as the first President. Most people forget that the Articles of Confederation was our constitution before our present Constitution was adopted in 1789 and Washington was elected.

Hanson did quite a bit during his brief tenure of office, from 1781 to 1782. First he proclaimed Thanksgiving Day in Massachusetts. He also established the departments of State, War, Navy, and Treasury, and set up a national judiciary, a post office, and a national bank.

A member of a well-known family of Swedish descent, he was a well-to-do plantation owner. He was elected probably because the Continental Congress had not put a Marylander into any responsible office, and they felt they owed that colony some recognition. He died in 1783.

Oddly enough, the life-size bronze statue in the U.S. Capitol doesn't look like him. We know Hanson's real appearance from several good portraits still existing. Apparently the statue's sculptor had his own ideas of what the first President of a new nation should look like.

Consequently, the statue looks more like the conventional idea of a handsome Hollywood leading man. Many people think it closely resembles the late movie star Robert Taylor. It shows "John Hanson" with a three-cornered hat on his head and an elegant cane in his left hand. In his right hand he holds an important-looking document chest high, as if about to read it.

It's a very impressive statue—but it isn't John Hanson.

UNIT 8
The Real First President

1. Most people in the U.S. will say the first President was—
   - (A) **Robert E. Lee**
   - (B) **Teddy Roosevelt**
   - (C) **Abraham Lincoln**
   - (D) **George Washington**

2. "John Hanson" might be an answer from a resident in—
   - (A) **Massachusetts**
   - (B) **Mississippi**
   - (C) **Maryland**
   - (D) **Missouri**

3. Connecting Washington with Annapolis is a John Hanson—
   - (A) **bridge**
   - (B) **highway**
   - (C) **tunnel**
   - (D) **railroad**

4. John Hanson was first elected by Congress as President in—
   - (A) **1681**
   - (B) **1770**
   - (C) **1871**
   - (D) **1781**

5. Hanson was in office for a period of—
   - (A) **one year**
   - (B) **five years**
   - (C) **four years**
   - (D) **three years**

6. For Massachusetts, he first proclaimed—
   - (A) **Veteran's Day**
   - (B) **Thanksgiving Day**
   - (C) **Memorial Day**
   - (D) **Labor Day**

7. He established the departments of State, Navy, Treasury, and—
   - (A) **Army**
   - (B) **Marines**
   - (C) **War**
   - (D) **Peace**

8. He also set up a national bank and—
   - (A) **pony express**
   - (B) **sheriff's office**
   - (C) **railroad service**
   - (D) **post office**

9. John Hanson died in—
   - (A) **1883**
   - (B) **1683**
   - (C) **1953**
   - (D) **1783**

10. Many people say the John Hanson statue resembles—
    - (A) **Robert Taylor**
    - (B) **Robert Young**
    - (C) **Robert Preston**
    - (D) **Robert Hope**

"I'll go," said the young woman one day many years ago. "I'll take the pack string up to the Neglected Mine." Frank Rivers looked at Olga Schaaf and hesitated. But he had no choice. It was the rainy season in Colorado, and the men working in the mine were waiting for supplies.

"Okay," said Rivers. "I'll pack the mules, and you'll just have to lead them to the mine. But be careful. The rains have washed out many of the trails."

That evening Olga arrived at the mine with her string of mules. But no woman had ever been there before, and Olga found no place to sleep. Cold and lonely, the brave young woman had to sit up all night.

The next day the superintendent of the mine told Olga that she should become a mule-train packer. "Men packers are scarce," he said, "and mule trains are the only way to get supplies and materials into the mines."

It was 1909; jobs for women paid very little, and Olga knew that packers earned twenty dollars a ton—around three hundred dollars a month. Without hesitation the plucky young woman took the job, and for the next forty years Olga Schaaf was known as the only female packer in the world.

During her lifetime Olga traveled to many mines in the Southwest and had exciting experiences. Once, three mules loaded with dynamite lost their footing and fell from Eagle Pass. The dynamite exploded harmlessly below. On one never-to-be-forgotten night she was snowed in at the Neglected Mine with sixteen miners and twenty-five mules. That night the temperature reached thirty degrees below zero. After four more days of freezing weather, the miners' food ran out. Many of the men were discouraged, but Olga Schaaf led them all to safety through snow that was sometimes ten feet deep.

In 1913 Olga met William Little at the Neglected Mine. After the two were married, William became a packer. Together, William and Olga increased their string of mules to forty. Bill Little died in 1969, and Olga lived just one year longer.

1. Olga Schaaf offered to go to—
   (A) town
   (B) the mine
   (C) get supplies
   (D) get the mules

2. The Neglected Mine was located in—
   (A) California
   (B) Canada
   (C) New Mexico
   (D) Colorado

3. Frank Rivers warned Olga that the trails might be—
   (A) dusty
   (B) foggy
   (C) washed away
   (D) freshly paved

4. That night Olga and her mules arrived at the mine—
   (A) safely
   (B) injured
   (C) in shock
   (D) hungry

5. In 1909 a mule-train packer earned—
   (A) $20 a pound
   (B) $200 a pound
   (C) $200 a ton
   (D) $20 a ton

6. Olga was known as the only female packer for—
   (A) forty days
   (B) fourteen years
   (C) forty years
   (D) four years

7. The mules that lost their footing on Eagle Pass were carrying—
   (A) bullets
   (B) dynamite
   (C) food
   (D) guns

8. Olga led the miners safely through—
   (A) snow
   (B) hail
   (C) rain
   (D) fog

9. In 1913 Olga married—
   (A) Frank Rivers
   (B) William Rivers
   (C) Frank Little
   (D) William Little

10. Together, Olga and her husband—
    (A) bought land in Denver
    (B) were packers
    (C) changed careers
    (D) increased their string of mules

UNIT 10
Selling from the Skies

When the First World War ended, there were hundreds of idle military airplanes and pilots. Advertisers, looking for unusual techniques, came up with the idea of selling from the sky. People could not avoid seeing the ads!

By 1919, for example, dropping leaflets from airplanes had actually become a public nuisance in England. At first people enjoyed scrambling to get the brightly colored pieces of paper that floated from the skies; finally they just ignored them.

Then smoke-writing became a fad. One British pilot spent years learning to "write and think backwards," which skywriting required. In 1922, flying a racing plane, this enterprising aviator spelled out a message over London. It was read by three million people over an area of a hundred square miles. This kind of smoke-writing is still seen occasionally in the United States.

Another idea never caught on, however. In New York in 1931, a searchlight of 91 million candle power projected an advertising message on the clouds over Brooklyn Bridge. Similar experiments were then tried in England. In one case, an ad was projected on a cloud fifteen miles away and could be read by countless people.

Defacing clouds seems bad enough, but even worse was an advertising technique called "sky-shouting." It was tried in America, Italy, and Sweden, and consisted of a low-flying airplane mounted with loudspeakers swooping overhead to deliver commercials. It has to be a frightening experience to have an airplane zoom down at you shouting, "Buy Old Blubber dog food," or some such thing!

Then came banner-towing airplanes and blimps with "electric spectacular" billboards. In 1949 sky-typing was invented. Seven planes would fly wing to wing and emit short bursts of smoke, often brightly colored, that when put together would spell out a message. The president of the sky-typing company bragged, "We can have the whole coast scribbled up in two hours."

To get away from advertisers, you can turn off the radio or TV, change channels or stations, or turn the newspaper page. But they know you can't turn off the sky!

UNIT 10
Selling from the Skies

1. Hundreds of military planes and pilots were idle after—
   (A) World War II
   (B) World War I
   (C) the Korean War
   (D) the Civil War

2. Advertisers thought of selling their products by using—
   (A) the ocean
   (B) songs
   (C) billboards
   (D) the sky

3. In 1919 dropping pamphlets became a nuisance in—
   (A) France
   (B) Egypt
   (C) England
   (D) Italy

4. After distributing pamphlets, advertisers used—
   (A) fire
   (B) smoke-writing
   (C) smoke bombs
   (D) flares

5. Skywriting requires a pilot to write—
   (A) frontwards
   (B) diagonally
   (C) sidewards
   (D) backwards

6. In London people who viewed the message numbered—
   (A) 300,000
   (B) 30,000,000
   (C) 3,000,000
   (D) 30,000

7. An advertising idea that didn't work was the use of—
   (A) flashlights
   (B) flares
   (C) searchlights
   (D) bonfires

8. The advertising message was projected on clouds over the—
   (A) Golden Gate Bridge
   (B) George Washington Bridge
   (C) Verrazano Bridge
   (D) Brooklyn Bridge

9. Sky-shouting used a low-flying plane and—
   (A) a microphone
   (B) loudspeakers
   (C) a TV
   (D) a radio

10. Sky-typing was invented in—
    (A) 1939
    (B) 1959
    (C) 1949
    (D) 1929

UNIT 11
Susan of Liberty Hall

Amid the industrial plants and superhighways of northeast New Jersey stands a tree-shaded mansion that recalls the long-gone years of the American Revolution—an era of violence and of bravery. The house recalls particularly the bravery of the quick-thinking young woman who saved it from destruction—and perhaps saved the American cause as well.

The mansion is Liberty Hall, near the city of Elizabeth. The woman was pert, vivacious Susan Livingston, the oldest daughter of the house's owner, New Jersey's governor William Livingston. So staunch a supporter of the Revolution was the governor that the British had put a price on his head, forcing him to keep shifting his location.

One midnight in 1779 a red-jacketed British force of a thousand, acting on a spy's tip that the governor was at Liberty Hall, surrounded the house. He wasn't there, but papers of immense value were. They were George Washington's own lists naming dozens of anti-British spies.

Susan Livingston watched as the Redcoats searched every corner of the house, coming ever closer to a cabinet containing the papers. She thought quickly.

Acting flustered, she begged the officer in charge, "Oh, sir, in this cabinet are extremely personal letters to me from a certain gentleman. If you will be gentleman enough not to look at them, I will show you where my father's papers are." Swayed by her charm and priding himself on his gentlemanliness, the officer did not open the cabinet. Susan then gave him the "papers": a worthless bundle of her father's old law briefs.

Susan's wit and courage were even more sorely tried a year later. Again refusing to abandon Liberty Hall to approaching enemy troops, Susan, her mother, and her sister suffered another midnight intrusion. This time, however, they faced not a gentleman officer but drunken soldiers bent on violence and destruction. Susan knew it was time not for charm but for action. In the flickering candlelight she grabbed the first attacker and threw him bodily down the stairs. The dazed soldiers, thinking the women were ghosts, fled in terror. No enemy ever bothered Liberty Hall again.

Liberty Hall is still owned today by descendants of the Livingstons. They and the nation are proud of the brave young woman who saved their ancestral home—and in saving Washington's secret papers may have helped set our country free.

1. The mansion dates back to the—
   - (A) Civil War
   - (B) Jamestown flood
   - (C) Battle of Waterloo
   - (D) American Revolution

2. Susan Livingston's father was a—
   - (A) journalist
   - (B) rancher
   - (C) scientist
   - (D) governor

3. Susan is described as pert, vivacious, and—
   - (A) sickly
   - (B) timid
   - (C) the oldest daughter
   - (D) domineering

4. The papers of value belonged to—
   - (A) George Washington
   - (B) Susan Livingston
   - (C) Oliver Cromwell
   - (D) Queen Elizabeth

5. The British soldiers were referred to as—
   - (A) Yellow Jackets
   - (B) Redcoats
   - (C) Green Berets
   - (D) Blue Angels

6. Susan begged for the letters, saying they were—
   - (A) of religious value
   - (B) treasured recipes
   - (C) extremely personal
   - (D) old bills

7. The papers Susan gave the officer were—
   - (A) wrapping paper
   - (B) lesson plans
   - (C) hidden treasure maps
   - (D) worthless law briefs

8. Liberty Hall, on the second occasion, was invaded by—
   - (A) gentlemen farmers
   - (B) drunken soldiers
   - (C) mischievous children
   - (D) a football team

9. Susan grabbed the attacker and—
   - (A) called for help
   - (B) pleaded for mercy
   - (C) beat him with a candlestick
   - (D) threw him down the stairs

10. Today Liberty Hall is—
    - (A) owned by the Livingston family
    - (B) a museum
    - (C) lying in ruins
    - (D) a shop

What animal is clever enough to let birds find dinner for it, can throw its voice and sing love songs in harmony, and is tough enough to increase in range and numbers despite being trapped, poisoned, and shot by those who regard it as a killer? This remarkable creature is the coyote.

Most of us know of coyotes only from the eerie "Owooooo!" that echoes from the nighttime hills in western movies. Usually the film's director uses the cry to suggest lonesomeness or a foreboding of danger.

Actually presenting no danger to humans, coyotes may sing in packs of two to ten, "harmonizing" so that no two maintain the same note. Parents may call to locate their offspring. "Come home, junior—right now!" may be the howled message.

Coyotes have a reputation for being clever—a quality they need to survive in a hostile environment. They have learned to avoid hunters' traps. In winter, when food is scarce, they watch where birds are flying, knowing that the birds have spotted an elk or deer to feed on. Often a coyote will "play possum" until a raven alights; then the coyote snaps up a tasty raven dinner. In their nocturnal howling coyotes can even throw their voices like ventriloquists, so that to enemies they seem at one instant a few yards away, the next instant a mile off. No wonder the Native American name for coyote means "trickster"!

Proof of the coyote's cleverness is that, in this age when humans have driven its cousin the wolf and so many other wild animals nearly to extinction, the coyote has managed not only to survive but to spread. It has been found as far east as Massachusetts, as far north as Hudson Bay, and as far south as Panama—in spite of vigorous efforts to exterminate it by some ranchers and farmers who believe it kills their livestock and poultry.

Is it really such a killer? Only if it cannot get food in the wild. Many naturalists believe that by eating rodents and other pests the coyote is more a friend to farmers than a foe.

UNIT 12
Harmonizer of the Hills

1. The clever animal in the story is described as being able to—
   (A) **find food for birds**
   (C) **sing love songs in harmony**
   (B) **shoot birds**
   (D) **poison an attacker**

2. This creature is called a—
   (A) **raven**
   (C) **wolf**
   (B) **koala bear**
   (D) **coyote**

3. The sound of its cry is said to be—
   (A) **hollow**
   (C) **almost inaudible**
   (B) **eerie**
   (D) **raucous**

4. To humans, coyotes present no threat of—
   (A) **danger**
   (C) **competition**
   (B) **companionship**
   (D) **thievery**

5. Parents call to locate their—
   (A) **cousins**
   (C) **hunter**
   (B) **orchestra**
   (D) **offspring**

6. Coyotes "play possum" in order to—
   (A) **avoid enemies**
   (C) **snap up food**
   (B) **trick humans**
   (D) **locate their offspring**

7. Coyotes howl during the—
   (A) **morning**
   (C) **afternoon**
   (B) **snowstorm**
   (D) **night**

8. The Native American name for coyote means—
   (A) **ventriloquist**
   (C) **enemy**
   (B) **trickster**
   (D) **hairy beast**

9. The coyote can be found as far north as—
   (A) **Hudson Bay**
   (C) **Massachusetts**
   (B) **Panama**
   (D) **California**

10. Naturalists consider the coyote to be a—
    (A) **rodent**
    (C) **killer**
    (B) **foe**
    (D) **friend**

In Unit 10 you read about how advertisers have used airplanes, and the sky, to sell their wares. Think about what you know about advertisements. Think about the ones that seem to catch your attention. What makes them "catchy"? Think, too, about the ads that you don't like or that don't seem to "grab" you. What makes them dull or ineffective? Read the following paragraphs about advertisements.

What is the purpose of an advertisement? Its main objective, of course, is to attract the buyers' attention so that they buy the product. You might think that its purpose is also to be creative, loud, colorful, beautiful, or even offensive. Because an advertisement must sell the product, it well may be any of *those* things, too.

What attracts people's attention? Sometimes it's a catchy phrase or jingle. Sometimes a striking or clever picture does the trick. To be really effective, however, most ads will use direct facts. Many ads that you see or hear rely on one of the following techniques: emotional appeal, bandwagon, testimonial, and repetition. Each technique has its own special elements or characteristics. For emotional appeal, the writer of the ad tries to get to you through your feelings by using emotion-laden words.

The bandwagon technique makes you think everyone else is using the product, so you should too. With a testimonial, advertisers want you to think that if someone you can identify with uses the product, it must be good. Ads may use repetition, the repeating of certain key words, so you will remember them—and remember the product. Regardless of what technique is used, an effective ad will contain facts rather than mere "fluff" in order to attract people's attention and get them interested in a product or service.

A. Exercising Your Skill

Think about what you know about advertisements and how they are written. Write facts about advertisements under the following column headings:

Important Qualities	Advertising Techniques
_____	_____
_____	_____

B. Expanding Your Skill

Think about how advertisements are written. Find an advertisement that demonstrates each technique and that uses facts in its presentation of a product or service. Look for examples in newspapers, in magazines, on radio, and on television. Compare your examples with those of your classmates.

C. Exploring Language

What are the important qualities in an advertisement? Think about what you know that helps make an ad successful. Then, after reading each of the following ads, write a sentence telling whether the ad "grabs" you, and why or why not. To what extent does the ad rely on facts? List the facts it tells you.

1. Who's behind that gorgeous pair of Panorama Sunglasses? Your favorite basketball star, Les Lookingood. Listen to Les: "I wear my blue Panorama Sunglasses everywhere. They're perfect for comfort *and* appearance. Strong, sturdy Panorama Sunglasses come with a money-back guarantee. Get a pair *today*!"

2. Buy a Roadbuster bike. Roadbusters are individually hand-crafted in our factory in New Mexico. Roadbusters offer speed, dependability, and endurance. Roadbusters are made of the newest lightweight metal alloys. For the best in bikes, remember the name—Roadbuster!

3. Everyone loves Yummy Gum! Made with real fruit juice, Yummy Gum is sugar-free and full of flavor. All America chews it—so don't be left out! Look for the gum in the bright purple wrapper. Buy a pack of Yummy Gum today!

Now, imagine that you are an internationally-known model. Your photograph has been in ads for everything from acne creams and herbal shampoos to the importance of using zip codes. Click Cameras wants you to endorse their equipment. Write a testimonial ad for Click Cameras. Be sure to make up a few facts about the product that would make people want to buy *this* particular type of camera.

D. Expressing Yourself

Choose one of these activities.

1. The earliest advertisements were probably street criers hawking the wares of shopkeepers. Find out five more facts about the history of advertising.

2. Work with one or two classmates to write and produce a radio or television advertisement. Pick any product, and use any advertising technique. "Perform" your ad for the rest of the class.

3. Choose one of the businesses below and design two newspaper ads for it. Each ad should use a different advertising technique. In addition to writing the copy, draw an accompanying illustration for each ad you created.

Polly's Perfect Pets	Fred's Flags
Klean-Kar Carwash	Browsers' Books

UNIT 13
An American Star

"No! No!" Ernest Belcher exclaimed, throwing up his hands in exasperation. The quiet little girl in leotards cringed. "Whoever taught you could have ruined your muscles. You must go back to the beginning and learn to dance all over again!"

Young Betty Marie Tallchief was crushed. She loved to dance, and she had been taking lessons in her hometown of Fairfax, Oklahoma, for three years—since she was five. Now in Los Angeles this new ballet teacher was telling her that all those hours of practice had been wasted.

But Betty Marie was no ordinary girl; she determined to start anew. Talented equally in piano and dance, and delighting equally in each, she willingly sacrificed her playtime to practice at both for hours daily after school. Her nimble fingers itched for the keyboard; her supple young legs quivered in anticipation of leaping and pirouetting to lilting music.

Betty Marie's background was not ordinary either. Her father was a wealthy Osage, Alexander Tallchief, and she was proud of her Native American heritage.

"You will be a great concert pianist," Betty Marie's ambitious mother declared—almost commanded. Yet as she grew toward beautiful womanhood, Betty felt the pull of the dance grow stronger. When the famous Russian ballet teacher, Madame Bronislava Nijinska, gave her a leading role, Betty Marie said to herself, "This will be my life, my road to success—the dance."

Success did come to Maria Tallchief—as she now called herself—but not without countless hours of toil, sweat, and pain. In New York she joined the Ballet Russe, where she danced mostly minor roles until there came that "big break" that every performer dreams of. Her swanlike grace and dazzling agility caught the eye of the great choreographer—dance creator—George Balanchine. Not only did he soon make her a star, he made her his wife. Betty Marie's wildest dreams had come true—and she was only twenty-one.

On both sides of the Atlantic—Paris and New York—audiences stood, cheered, and threw bouquets when Maria stepped to the footlights to take her bows. Her most famous role, created by Balanchine, was that of the magical Firebird.

The years of hard work had borne fruit for the quiet Osage girl from Oklahoma. She had become the first modern-day American to win international acclaim as a prima ballerina!

1. When Belcher spoke, the quiet girl in leotards—
    (A) **giggled**   (B) **screeched**
    (C) **curtsied**   (D) **cringed**

2. Betty's hometown was in—
    (A) **California**   (B) **Canada**
    (C) **Oklahoma**   (D) **Mexico**

3. When Belcher first saw Betty dance, she had been taking lessons for—
    (A) **eight years**   (B) **three years**
    (C) **five years**   (D) **twelve years**

4. Besides dancing, Betty showed equal talent for the—
    (A) **piano**   (B) **drums**
    (C) **crafts**   (D) **language arts**

5. To allow time for dance and piano practice, Betty sacrificed her—
    (A) **playtime**   (B) **dinnertime**
    (C) **playthings**   (D) **allowance**

6. Betty's father was a—
    (A) **migrant farmer**   (B) **ballet teacher**
    (C) **tall chief**   (D) **wealthy Osage**

7. The teacher who influenced Betty to dance professionally was—
    (A) **Chinese**   (B) **French**
    (C) **American**   (D) **Russian**

8. George Balanchine, the choreographer, became Betty's—
    (A) **competitor**   (B) **manager**
    (C) **husband**   (D) **enemy**

9. Betty performed in the United States and—
    (A) **Egypt**   (B) **Europe**
    (C) **Africa**   (D) **Australia**

10. Her most famous role was—
    (A) **Sleeping Beauty**   (B) **Golfo**
    (C) **Firebird**   (D) **Giselle**

UNIT 14
It Sounds Like . . .

You're sitting in an airport, waiting for the announcement that your flight to Oakland is ready to board. You hear the announcement, walk to the gate, and hand the flight attendant a boarding pass. The plane takes off, and the pilot starts talking about the flight. Then you realize that you are on the wrong plane, heading thousands of miles in the wrong direction.

This could be a dream—and perhaps you've had a similar one—but this was no dream to Michael Lewis.

Lewis was a twenty-one-year-old college student in 1985 when he began a trip home to Oakland, California, from London, England. It was an uneventful flight aboard the plane. The flight landed in Los Angeles, and Lewis left the plane. He needed to change planes and take another flight for the one-hour trip to Oakland.

A flight attendant asked him if he was going to Aukland. Michael Lewis, thinking she had said "Oakland," said yes. She handed him a boarding pass. The flight was announced, and Lewis boarded the plane. It wasn't until the plane was in the air that he realized he was heading in the wrong direction. At first, no one would believe him.

The flight, of course, continued on to Aukland, New Zealand. It was a twelve-hour flight that covered 6,500 miles. The plane touched down just once, in Tahiti. During his eight hours in Aukland, Lewis took a bus tour of the city and decided that Aukland was actually a pretty nice place. Then he boarded a plane back to Los Angeles. From there he caught a plane to Oakland.

The moral of the story: Listen carefully. Lewis misunderstood what he had heard. It could have been a costly mistake. The round-trip plane fare between Los Angeles and Aukland at the time was $2,064. Fortunately, the airline didn't charge Lewis a penny.

UNIT 14
It Sounds Like . . .

1. Michael Lewis was—
   (A) twelve years old
   (B) twenty-one years old
   (C) twenty-five years old
   (D) thirty-one years old

2. The event took place in—
   (A) 1589
   (B) 1895
   (C) 1958
   (D) 1985

3. Michael Lewis was a—
   (A) pilot
   (B) bus driver
   (C) flight attendant
   (D) college student

4. Lewis' trip home began in—
   (A) Oakland, California
   (B) Aukland, New Zealand
   (C) London, England
   (D) Los Angeles, California

5. Lewis intended to take a second flight to—
   (A) Aukland
   (B) Los Angeles
   (C) Tahiti
   (D) Oakland

6. The second flight would take—
   (A) one hour
   (B) eight hours
   (C) twelve hours
   (D) twenty hours

7. Lewis realized his mistake—
   (A) in the airport
   (B) in Oakland
   (C) when the plane was in the air
   (D) when the plane landed in New Zealand

8. The flight to New Zealand covered—
   (A) 65 miles
   (B) 6,500 miles
   (C) 650 miles
   (D) 65,000 miles

9. Michael Lewis confused—
   (A) Oakland with Aukland
   (B) Oakland with Okay
   (C) Aukland with Austin
   (D) Austin with Oakland

10. The round-trip fare between Los Angeles and Aukland was—
    (A) $2.06
    (B) $20.64
    (C) $206.40
    (D) $2,064

UNIT 15
Just Where Are You?

You leave Denver, Colorado, and drive west on Interstate 70. You pass an exit for the towns of Black Hawk and Idaho Springs. Now you're heading through the Rocky Mountains. You pass Argo Mill Historical Mining Site. Twenty minutes later you approach the exit for Arapaho Basin Ski Area. Then you're literally going into the mountains as you drive through the Eisenhower Memorial Tunnel. Several minutes later, at Exit 201, you leave the interstate and take state Route 9 south. Nine miles later, deep in the Rocky Mountains, you're in the town of Breckenridge. Where are you?

Look on a road map. These places are there. This is *not* a riddle.

You may be in the Breckenridge area, but that area may *not* be in the United States for three days a year. Or, if you're actually in Breckenridge, you may *not* be in the United States at all. Sound perplexing? You bet it is.

The Colorado Historical Society says that long ago a surveyor made an error. Consequently, a piece of land thirty miles wide and ninety miles long belonged to no one. It became a no-man's-land but legally may have become part of the United States in 1936. It was decided at the time, however, that that land should keep "the right to be a free and independent kingdom three days each year."

The United States General Land Office agrees that there is an area in Colorado, west of Denver, that was not part of the Louisiana Purchase in 1803 nor part of the annexation of Texas in 1845. Also, that office says, it was not acquired by the United States through any treaties made with the Ute Indians (Native Americans). The Utes say they never had any claim to it.

So, what does this mean?

It may mean nothing at all. It may be a mystery that is never solved. It may also mean that people born in Breckenridge are actually not citizens of the United States.

1. To get to Breckenridge, you leave Denver on—
   (A) **Interstate 9**   (B) **Route 70**
   (C) **Interstate 70**   (D) **Route 9**

2. You drive through—
   (A) **Black Hawk**   (B) **Idaho Springs**
   (C) **the Arapaho Basin Ski Area**   (D) **the Eisenhower Memorial Tunnel**

3. The distance along Route 9 to Breckenridge is—
   (A) **several miles**   (B) **twenty miles**
   (C) **nine miles**   (D) **two-hundred miles**

4. Breckenridge is deep in the—
   (A) **Idaho Springs**   (B) **Rocky Mountains**
   (C) **Eisenhower Tunnel**   (D) **White Mountains**

5. The Breckenridge area may not be in the United States—
   (A) **three days a year**   (B) **nine days a year**
   (C) **thirty days a year**   (D) **ninety days a year**

6. The Colorado Historical Society says a mistake was made by a—
   (A) **miner**   (B) **king**
   (C) **historian**   (D) **surveyor**

7. The land legally may have become part of the United States in—
   (A) **1970**   (B) **1936**
   (C) **1963**   (D) **1907**

8. The area in question is located—
   (A) **in Texas**   (B) **west of Denver**
   (C) **north of Idaho Springs**   (D) **in Louisiana**

9. The group that denied having any claim to the land was the—
   (A) **Utes**   (B) **Cheyennes**
   (C) **Arapahos**   (D) **Apaches**

10. People born in Breckenridge may not actually be—
    (A) **free**   (B) **citizens of a kingdom**
    (C) **part of a mystery**   (D) **United States citizens**

UNIT 16
To a Hair Specialist

In the early 1800s there were barber shops for men but no places for women to have their hair cared for. In 1857 the founder of beauty shops for women was born. Her family was poor, and before she was ten she was sent to live with another family to work as a servant.

The girl was Martha Harper. She began to form definite ideas about hair care. These ideas were very advanced for the late 1800s and early 1900s. The kind doctor for whom Martha worked as a young girl of ten taught Martha his then revolutionary method of hair and scalp care.

For centuries before this, hair washing had been rare. Instead of washing, powders were applied liberally to hide the dirt, mask the odor, and sometimes cover up the vermin that often thrived in long locks. The doctor for whom Martha worked had developed a complex herbal hair tonic and some excellent hygienic procedures. From him Martha learned the benefits of scalp massage and repeated hair brushing using castile suds. When the doctor died, he left his herbal formula to Martha.

In 1875, at eighteen, Martha Harper set out for the city of Rochester, New York, to open her first beauty parlor. It wasn't easy. Landlords questioned her: "What kind of business? A beauty shop! What's that?" Many refused to rent space to her, but she finally succeeded in finding a place.

She herself was her best advertisement. She had long, thick hair that reached the floor, but instead of looking unkempt it was beautifully cared for and remarkably clean. Her business thrived.

When Harper hired help, their training included her philosophy: "Make the customer feel good." Harper wanted the customer to relax and enjoy the treatment.

That first shop was the beginning of a chain of Harper salons. Movie stars who later patronized them included the Marx Brothers and Helen Hayes.

Today there are thousands of shops for both women and men that specialize in washing, cutting, permanent-waving, coloring, and styling hair. Hair grooming has come a long way since 1875, when Martha Harper got it off to such a good start.

UNIT 16
To a Hair Specialist

1. Men of the 1800s could have their hair cared for in—
   (A) replacement centers
   (B) unisex haircutting shops
   (C) barber shops
   (D) beauty salons

2. The founder of beauty shops for women was—
   (A) Harper Woods
   (B) Martha Harper
   (C) Ida Harper
   (D) Martha Custis

3. A doctor taught his servant girl his method of—
   (A) hair and scalp care
   (B) dressing wounds
   (C) bloodletting
   (D) laser surgery

4. Before the middle 1800s hair was not usually—
   (A) curled
   (B) powdered
   (C) braided
   (D) washed

5. The doctor left Martha his—
   (A) surgical tools
   (B) office supplies
   (C) herbal formula
   (D) medical kit

6. In 1875 Harper opened her first beauty parlor in—
   (A) Rome, New York
   (B) Rochester, New York
   (C) Rochester, Minnesota
   (D) Raleigh, North Carolina

7. Her best advertisement was her own well kept—
   (A) office
   (B) skin
   (C) home
   (D) hair

8. Martha's philosophy was to make the customer—
   (A) overconfident
   (B) jealous
   (C) downcast
   (D) comfortable

9. Some famous customers of Harper salons were—
   (A) mountain climbers
   (B) state senators
   (C) movie stars
   (D) army officers

10. Hair salons of today provide services for—
    (A) men only
    (B) men and women
    (C) dolls
    (D) women only

UNIT 17
The Lucky Flower

While William McKinley was campaigning for re-election to the presidency of the United States in 1900, he began wearing a red carnation. Winning the election, he decided then and there that the red carnation was his lucky flower, and he began wearing one wherever he went, even after being inaugurated as President.

In 1901 a twelve-year-old girl named Myrtle Ledger was taken by her parents to the Pan-American Exposition in Buffalo, New York, to see the wonders of that enormous fair.

Mr. McKinley arrived at the fair on the same day, cheered by crowds. He stood in a building called the Temple of Music, wearing his lucky red carnation, as thousands lined up to shake his hand.

Myrtle Ledger was in that line, but she couldn't see very much because she was so little. She was very disappointed, because she had worn her prettiest dress to see the President. When Myrtle complained to her mother that she couldn't get near the President, a young man offered to take her to meet him. Her mother gave permission.

The young man put Myrtle down in a good spot in the line of people waiting to shake hands with Mr. McKinley. Soon she was face to face with the President.

When Mr. McKinley asked the child her name, she told him it was Myrtle. Myrtle, of course, is also the name of a pretty flower. So the President said, "In that case, I must give this flower to another little flower." He took his red carnation from his jacket and gave it to the little girl.

Naturally, Myrtle felt delighted and lucky to get such a souvenir. But luck was not with the President that day, for not far behind the little girl in the waiting line stood a shabby man with a gun hidden under a bandage on his right hand. As he came to the President, he fired twice. Mr. McKinley died from the wounds—without his lucky red flower.

1. In 1900 William McKinley was running for—
   - (A) governor
   - (B) mayor
   - (C) President
   - (D) Vice-president

2. After winning the election he decided the red carnation brought—
   - (A) illness
   - (B) good luck
   - (C) bad luck
   - (D) misfortune

3. Myrtle Ledger's age in 1901 was—
   - (A) twenty years
   - (B) seven years
   - (C) ten years
   - (D) twelve years

4. The Pan-American Exposition was held in—
   - (A) Syracuse
   - (B) Monticello
   - (C) Buffalo
   - (D) Boston

5. Mr. McKinley was surrounded by crowds in the Temple of—
   - (A) Science
   - (B) Music
   - (C) Inventions
   - (D) Dance

6. Myrtle was led to meet Mr. McKinley by—
   - (A) a woman
   - (B) her father
   - (C) a man
   - (D) her mother

7. Myrtle is also the name of a—
   - (A) tree
   - (B) garden
   - (C) river
   - (D) flower

8. McKinley gave Myrtle his—
   - (A) glove
   - (B) rose
   - (C) carnation
   - (D) jacket

9. A shabby man had a hidden—
   - (A) knife
   - (B) gun
   - (C) flower
   - (D) bomb

10. The man wounded McKinley—
    - (A) ten times
    - (B) three times
    - (C) once
    - (D) two times

John Montagu, the fourth Earl of Sandwich, liked to play cards. In fact, once, in 1762, he played for twenty-four hours straight. He refused to leave a game, even to eat. Instead, he had his meals brought to him. What did he eat? Thin slices of meat and cheese between two pieces of bread. The sandwich was born. What could be simpler?

Josephine Cochrane never washed a dish in her life. She was the wife of an Illinois politician. The Cochranes were wealthy and had servants who did all the cooking and cleaning—including washing dishes. By the mid 1880s, though, Cochrane was upset by the number of dishes that became broken by being washed by hand.

Josephine Cochrane measured her cups, saucers, and plates. For every type of dish, she used wire to form individual sections of a rack, which was attached to a wheel. As a motor turned the wheel, soapy water sprayed from a water boiler over the dishes. The dishwasher was born. What could be simpler?

Earle Dickson worked for a company that packaged large individual gauze pads. These bandages were germ-free, thus reducing the danger of infection. They were sent to hospitals everywhere and were used to dress wounds after surgery.

Earle Dickson's wife often cut herself while cooking, the cuts being much too small for the gauze pads. So, in 1920, Dickson cut a small piece of a gauze pad and placed it in the center of a strip of sticky tape. He made up a lot of these small bandages at a time. The adhesive bandage was born. What could be simpler?

Walter Hunt needed some money to pay a debt of fifteen dollars. He realized suddenly that what the world needed was a pin that would hold clothes together but would be safe to use. It wouldn't stick the person using it. In three hours he designed his fastener, which was made from a single piece of wire. The catch on the fastener guarded the point of the pin. He sold his design for $400. The safety pin was born. What could be simpler?

1. John Montagu was—
   - (A) an admiral
   - (B) an Illinois politician
   - (C) a card player
   - (D) the Earl of Sandwich

2. Between two pieces of bread Montagu liked—
   - (A) tuna fish
   - (B) peanut butter and jelly
   - (C) meat and cheese
   - (D) cucumbers

3. Josephine Cochrane was upset by the number of—
   - (A) dirty dishes
   - (B) Illinois politicians
   - (C) household servants
   - (D) broken dishes

4. Josephine Cochrane made a rack from—
   - (A) water
   - (B) cups, saucers, and plates
   - (C) cotton batting
   - (D) wire

5. Soapy water sprayed from a—
   - (A) dish rack
   - (B) water wheel
   - (C) water boiler
   - (D) broken dish

6. Earle Dickson's wife often—
   - (A) cut herself
   - (B) washed dishes
   - (C) cooked
   - (D) dressed up

7. Dickson put a piece of a gauze pad in the center of—
   - (A) a cut finger
   - (B) a strip of sticky tape
   - (C) a cotton dressing
   - (D) a large wound

8. Earle Dickson first made the small bandages in—
   - (A) 1762
   - (B) 1880
   - (C) 1920
   - (D) 1960

9. Walter Hunt owed someone—
   - (A) four hundred dollars
   - (B) twenty dollars
   - (C) one hundred dollars
   - (D) fifteen dollars

10. Hunt designed his fastener in—
    - (A) one hour
    - (B) two hours
    - (C) four hours
    - (D) three hours

UNIT 19
What's the Harm?

Australia has some of the most fascinating animals on Earth. There is one problem, though. Australia also has more poisonous or dangerous animals than anywhere else.

The bite of the funnel-web spider causes vomiting, rising blood pressure, and in some cases, coma. Antivenom is available, and anyone who gets quick treatment can be saved. Unfortunately for humans, funnel web spiders like to live in suburban gardens! However, the spider is very shy and only bites under extreme pressure.

When you think of dangerous snakes you probably think of a rattlesnake or a cobra. Australia has nineteen species of snakes more poisonous than a rattlesnake. And it has eleven species more toxic than a cobra! The most toxic snake on Earth is the fierce snake. A full dose of its venom could kill 250,000 mice. But there is good news. This snake rarely comes in contact with human beings because it lives in nonpopulated areas.

Australians love to swim. But one of the most dangerous animals lives in the water. The box jellyfish can kill within minutes of its sting. People who survive its sting often have permanent scars. Australians know that the jellyfish is common in the summer at northern beaches, so they stay out of its way!

Can an animal be both fascinating and fearsome? The crocodile certainly qualifies. The saltwater crocodile is one of only two species that attacks human beings without being provoked. Swimmers in the ocean and farther inland where salt water reaches are very careful of this animal. Yet despite the danger, Australians have worked hard to protect the "saltie," which was near extinction at one time.

Actually, if you consider how many animals humans kill every day, perhaps the risk of spiders, snakes, and crocodiles is not so great. Especially when most of them don't attack first!

UNIT 19
What's the Harm?

1. Many Australian animals are both fascinating and—
   (A) fast
   (B) dangerous
   (C) extinct
   (D) colorful

2. The bite of the funnel-web spider can be treated with—
   (A) blood pressure medicine
   (B) aspirin
   (C) tourniquets
   (D) antivenom

3. The funnel-web spider rarely bites humans, because it is—
   (A) hard to see
   (B) out of poison
   (C) aggressive
   (D) shy

4. The most toxic snake on Earth is the—
   (A) cobra
   (B) rattlesnake
   (C) fierce snake
   (D) copperhead

5. The Australian fierce snake mostly lives in—
   (A) unpopulated areas
   (B) suburban gardens
   (C) seashore areas
   (D) laboratories

6. Australian swimmers in the north look out for—
   (A) the fierce snake
   (B) the funnel-web spider
   (C) the cobra
   (D) the box jellyfish

7. People who survive the jellyfish's sting often have—
   (A) fevers
   (B) nightmares
   (C) scars
   (D) flashbacks

8. The saltwater crocodile will attack a person without—
   (A) clothing
   (B) provocation
   (C) weapons
   (D) looking

9. Australians have saved the "saltie" from—
   (A) swimming
   (B) poisons
   (C) eating
   (D) extinction

10. Actually, the most dangerous animal on Earth is the—
    (A) rattlesnake
    (B) crocodile
    (C) human being
    (D) elephant

In some way, every day, flowers touch our lives. We may see flowers in our neighborhoods, flowers in the parks, flowers in pictures and paintings, and flowers printed on fabric or wallpaper. While flowers for most people may be a luxury, President McKinley (Unit 17) certainly thought that flowers—at least one, his red carnation—was a necessity. Think about what you know about flowers and how they are grown. Then read the following paragraph.

Many places on earth have an abundance of wild flowering plants, so wanting to have flowers growing around us is not a new idea. The Greeks planted small gardens of green grasses mixed with wild-flowers. In the Middle Ages, which were often referred to as "Dark," wildflowers added brightness. They not only grew wild, but they were also grown in gardens. Plants, including herbs, were grown for medicines. And gardeners have always known that flowers (or plants of any kind) need the right kind of soil and certain amounts of water and sunlight to grow well. Not all flowers need the same amounts, however, and that is what is tricky about growing flowers—and what has always separated the "green thumbs" from the weed growers!

A. Exercising Your Skill

Think about what you know about flowers. Make three lists. In one, write the names of several flowers you know. In another, write some uses for flowers and plants. In the last, write a list of places where you could find flowers. Give each of your lists an appropriate heading. Compare your lists with your classmates' lists.

B. Expanding Your Skill

Find out some facts about five of the flowers listed in the box. Then make a chart. Copy the five headings given. List the names of the five flowers you chose and the facts you collected about them under the appropriate headings. You might also want to add to the chart some other flowers that you know of or that are popular in your region of the country.

marigold	lily of the valley	daffodil
petunia	hibiscus	hollyhock
daisy	violet	swamp iris
snapdragon	tulip	sunflower

Flower	Color(s)	Height	Soil	Sun or Shade
_____	_____	_____	_____	_____
_____	_____	_____	_____	_____

C. Exploring Language

Think of what you know about flowers and the conditions needed for growing them. Using those facts, plan a small flower garden such as a window box and write about it. Describe the location, how you might need to change or fertilize the soil, and how you would arrange your garden. Draw a diagram of your garden that also shows its location and the arrangement of the flowers. Then create a schedule of planting times, watering times, and possibly even fertilizing times for your garden.

D. Expressing Yourself

Choose one of these activities.

1. What do you remember about President McKinley and Myrtle in the story "The Lucky Flower"? Write about what you think might have happened to Myrtle after meeting President McKinley. Did she see the man who shot the President? What did she do with the flower McKinley had given her? Or, write about what would have happened if President McKinley hadn't stopped to give Myrtle the flower.

2. President McKinley considered a red carnation to be lucky. Do you have something that you consider lucky? Write about a lucky charm you have or something you do to bring you luck (like wearing a favorite sweater on the day you take a test). How did that item, or habit, become "lucky" to you?

3. Words have meanings. We all know that. When we read "table," for instance, an object comes to mind. If we read "rose," an image of a certain flower will probably come to mind. But many flowers, roses included, have other meanings. A white rose means "silence," but a yellow rose means "jealousy." Find out what these flowers mean:

blue violet	petunia
orchid	lily of the valley
forget-me-not	tulip

UNIT 20
Wanderers of the Skies

How old do you have to be to have a pilot's license? If you wish to pilot a hot-air balloon, you can take the test at sixteen. At fourteen you can obtain a learner's certificate.

Balloons have become very popular throughout the country in the last few decades, ever since small gas burners were developed and lightweight nylon replaced bulky, hard-to-handle cotton. The burners heat the air that fills the balloons and makes them rise.

Many balloon pilots use a fan to blow the heated air into the balloon. As the huge balloon fills with hot air, it pulls upward. In fact, it tugs so hard it has to be held down by ropes until the pilot is ready to fly. A fully inflated balloon may be six stories high.

Under the balloon is a basket called a gondola, which generally can hold up to four people. When the pilot is ready, the people holding the ground ropes let go, and it's up, up, and away.

Balloons cannot be controlled like planes; the pilot can govern only up and down movement. Otherwise balloons move wherever the breeze takes them.

The popularity of ballooning has mushroomed so greatly that now there is a world hot-air-balloon championship competition held every other year in a different nation. Owners gather with all sorts of colorful balloons, some painted with figures, others with stripes, and perhaps even one or two looking like patchwork quilts. There is also a balloon fair each October in Albuquerque, New Mexico, where open space and light winds provide ideal ballooning conditions. Over three hundred balloons take part.

Ballooning was humankind's first way of flying. It began two centuries ago in 1783 in France. The first flight managed to stay aloft for ten whole minutes. That started a ballooning fad. During this period people tried to outdo each other. One designed a balloon that looked like a ship. Another ascended on horseback! Tickets were sold to spectators who wanted to watch the "crazy" stunts. The balloonists themselves were serious, thinking that ballooning would be the travel of the future.

Of course, they found that the balloons couldn't be steered. Skilled pilots might catch an air current in the direction they wanted to go, but the steering had no accuracy.

Imagine air travel today if it had stopped with balloons. Buy a ticket for London and you might land in Egypt!

1. A test for piloting a balloon can be taken at age—
    - (A) fifteen
    - (B) twelve
    - (C) sixteen
    - (D) twenty

2. In the balloons cotton has been replaced by—
    - (A) silk
    - (B) satin
    - (C) rayon
    - (D) nylon

3. The burners on the balloons use—
    - (A) gas
    - (B) oil
    - (C) coal
    - (D) sulphur

4. Heat from these burners makes the balloon—
    - (A) spin
    - (B) rise
    - (C) descend
    - (D) change direction

5. The balloons are tied down by—
    - (A) chains
    - (B) pipes
    - (C) ropes
    - (D) wires

6. The gondola is a balloon—
    - (A) burner
    - (B) boat
    - (C) sail
    - (D) basket

7. Balloons may even be painted like—
    - (A) quilts
    - (B) planes
    - (C) rockets
    - (D) blankets

8. Each October a balloon fair is held in—
    - (A) New York
    - (B) New Zealand
    - (C) New Jersey
    - (D) New Mexico

9. Ballooning began two hundred years ago in—
    - (A) Spain
    - (B) France
    - (C) England
    - (D) Italy

10. Pilots found that the balloons couldn't—
    - (A) go up
    - (B) go down
    - (C) be steered
    - (D) float

Five times on April 14, 1912, warnings had been received of icebergs ahead, but neither the crew nor the passengers were alarmed. This was the maiden voyage of the *Titanic*, bound for New York. Why worry about ice? The *Titanic* was unsinkable!

Captain Smith smiled as he thought about the new safety feature. The *Titanic*'s hull was divided into waterproof compartments. Even if it should strike ice, one or two compartments might fill with water, but the ship would not sink. A sixth warning was received. Captain Smith smiled again and went to bed.

Then suddenly a towering iceberg loomed up out of the dark. There was a slight shudder below. Cardplayers glanced up briefly. Curious, a few of them strolled out on deck. The *Titanic* seemed as safe and secure as ever.

However, things were quite different below. The iceberg had ripped a three-hundred-foot gash in the hull. Quickly the builder of the ship spelled out the bad news to the unbelieving Captain Smith. Too many waterproof compartments had filled. The "unsinkable" ship could not stay afloat.

Captain Smith ordered crew members to put passengers into lifeboats. To his dismay, most passengers refused to take the situation seriously. Some refused to get out of bed. Others continued to enjoy their parties. Meanwhile thousands of gallons of water were pouring into the ship every minute.

Then the captain remembered another chilling fact. There were lifeboats for only 1,178 persons; yet there were 2,201 aboard.

Finally, as the boat began to list, passengers understood their plight. There were many cases of bravery. Men on deck calmly waved farewel¹ to their wives in lifeboats. The band played the latest ragtime tunes. Some cardplayers calmly returned to their games—to play to the end.

At 2:20 A.M. the mighty *Titanic* stood on end, lights ablaze. Then it slipped beneath the waters. Captain Smith and 1,506 others were washed into the freezing sea. Within forty minutes they perished. The unsinkable ship had sunk.

1. This event took place in—
   (A) **May 1932** (B) **April 1912**
   (C) **June 1913** (D) **March 1922**

2. The *Titanic* was considered unsinkable because it had—
   (A) **pumps** (B) **an airtight hull**
   (C) **waterproof compartments** (D) **a steel hull**

3. The total number of warnings received was—
   (A) **five** (B) **three**
   (C) **six** (D) **four**

4. When Captain Smith received the last warning, he—
   (A) **yawned** (B) **smiled**
   (C) **frowned** (D) **laughed**

5. When the *Titanic* shuddered, the cardplayers—
   (A) **ignored it** (B) **glanced up**
   (C) **smiled** (D) **shouted**

6. The gash in the hull was—
   (A) **300 feet** (B) **600 feet**
   (C) **400 feet** (D) **200 feet**

7. The captain learned the bad news from the—
   (A) **cardplayers** (B) **cook**
   (C) **lookout** (D) **builder**

8. There were lifeboats for only—
   (A) **1,000 persons** (B) **500 persons**
   (C) **1,178 persons** (D) **2,207 persons**

9. The *Titanic* went down at—
   (A) **2:20 A.M.** (B) **3:00 P.M.**
   (C) **7:00 A.M.** (D) **4:20 A.M.**

10. Captain Smith and 1,506 others perished within—
    (A) **four minutes** (B) **four days**
    (C) **one week** (D) **forty minutes**

UNIT 22
Please Don't Break the Flowers

You wander through the garden. You look at flowers from an apple tree in varying stages of blossoming. You see flowers from mountain climates blooming near orchids usually found in the tropics. For a year you visit the garden every day it is open. The flowers are always blooming, perfectly cared for.

How can this be? What is the gardener's secret? Where *is* this magical place? Where are you?

You are indeed in a magical place, but it's not secret, just not widely known. You're visiting the Ware Glass Flower Collection at Harvard University. Yes, the flowers are glass, perfect replicas of the real thing.

The Glass Flower collection first opened to the public in 1893. Today as many as 200,000 people a year visit the museum in Cambridge, Massachusetts, to marvel at the flowers.

It is the only place in the world where you can look at absolutely to-scale models of samples of plants from all around the world. Each flower is exact in scale, detail, and color.

The flowers were formed in glass by hand—petal by petal, stem by stem—by Leopold and Rudolph Blaschka, a father-and-son team of glassworkers who lived in Germany. Some of the models have well over a hundred separate parts. The colors in each part were stained into molten glass.

The idea for the glass flowers started with a Harvard botany professor, G.L. Goodale. He wanted actual flower specimens to use with his students. Actual flowers wither and die. Glass flowers do not.

There are more than three thousand models in the Ware Collection. Some models show whole flowers. Others are magnified details of flower parts. Still other models show how plants are fertilized by insects or how diseases affect certain fruits.

The Blaschkas spent nearly fifty years, from 1887 to 1936, completing the collection. It is their life's work.

1. The Ware Glass Flower Collection can be found at—
   (A) **Cambridge University**
   (B) **Harvard University**
   (C) **Massachusetts College**
   (D) **the University of Germany**

2. The collection first opened to the public in—
   (A) **1993**
   (B) **1939**
   (C) **1893**
   (D) **1839**

3. Today the collection is visited yearly by as many as—
   (A) **200 people**
   (B) **2,000 people**
   (C) **20,000 people**
   (D) **200,000 people**

4. The flowers were formed by—
   (A) **machine**
   (B) **hand**
   (C) **whittling**
   (D) **blowing**

5. Leopold and Rudolph Blaschka were—
   (A) **father and son**
   (B) **brothers**
   (C) **uncle and nephew**
   (D) **grandfather and grandson**

6. The Blaschkas lived in—
   (A) **Massachusetts**
   (B) **Harvard**
   (C) **Cambridge**
   (D) **Germany**

7. The colors of the glass flowers were—
   (A) **dyed into the glass**
   (B) **sprayed on**
   (C) **stained into molten glass**
   (D) **painted on by hand**

8. The idea for the flowers came from G.L. Goodale, who was a—
   (A) **museum director**
   (B) **glassworker**
   (C) **student**
   (D) **botany professor**

9. The number of models in the collection exceeds—
   (A) **30**
   (B) **300**
   (C) **3,000**
   (D) **3 million**

10. To complete the collection, it took the Blaschkas nearly—
    (A) **eighteen years**
    (B) **thirty years**
    (C) **five years**
    (D) **fifty years**

In 1590, when Governor John White stepped ashore on his return to Roanoke Island, a heart-sinking silence greeted him. "Where are my people," he moaned, "—my daughter, her baby?"

Pushing inland to where the colonists' small settlement had been, White encountered, behind recently erected barricades, only weed-covered foundations. The crude log homes had been taken down—not destroyed. The boats, weapons, and meager supplies of the 119 English colonists were gone as well. So were the colonists—every last one of them. Yet there were no signs of a struggle, nor any corpses. White was both saddened and mystified.

Led by White, the small band of English men and women had first landed on Roanoke, off the North Carolina coast, three years earlier, intending to establish England's first permanent New World colony. Within days they celebrated the first birth of an English child on American soil—White's granddaughter, Virginia Dare. But they soon realized that for them to survive, the governor would have to sail back to England for more supplies and for weapons.

It had been agreed before White's departure that if lack of food or threat of attack forced the colonists to move, they would write their destination in a conspicuous place. If in great danger, they would mark a cross above the name.

In England wars and bureaucracy had delayed White's return for three years. Now, trudging forlornly through the deserted settlement, White groped for a clue to his companions' fate. Then he came upon a tree into which had been carved a single word: Croatoan. There was no cross over it. He knew that Croatoan was another island along the coast. Yet stormy seas and his ship's rebellious crew prevented him from searching there.

To this day no trace of the lost colonists has ever been found. For years it was thought that they had been slaughtered by hostile Indians or the Spanish. The lack of battle evidence, however, renders these theories unlikely. Today many believe that the colonists sought refuge with friendly Hatteras Indians on Croatoan Island when threatened by hostile groups. In 1709 a historian recorded seeing gray-eyed, lighter-skinned Hatteras Indians. Some of their names sounded like English names.

Were these the descendants of the Roanoke colonists? No one can be sure.

1. Governor John White returned to Roanoke Island in—
   (A) **1590**
   (B) **1950**
   (C) **1638**
   (D) **1980**

2. He was mainly concerned about his—
   (A) **wife and son**
   (B) **mother-in-law**
   (C) **fiancée**
   (D) **daughter and her baby**

3. Behind barricades there were—
   (A) **log homes**
   (B) **weed-covered foundations**
   (C) **boats and weapons**
   (D) **meager food supplies**

4. The colony had previously numbered—
   (A) **178 people**
   (B) **47 English officers**
   (C) **119 settlers**
   (D) **101 children**

5. White was very sad and confused when he found—
   (A) **a circus troupe**
   (B) **many corpses**
   (C) **Indians**
   (D) **no one**

6. Three years earlier his daughter had given birth to—
   (A) **Virginia Dare**
   (B) **Pocahontas**
   (C) **Bob White**
   (D) **Virginia White**

7. The colonists agreed that if danger befell they would—
   (A) **burn the village**
   (B) **build a fort**
   (C) **mark a cross above a destination**
   (D) **send a telegram**

8. White was detained in England for—
   (A) **eight years**
   (B) **a few weeks**
   (C) **three months**
   (D) **three years**

9. After searching, he came upon a message that read—
   (A) **Algonquin**
   (B) **Iroquois**
   (C) **Croatoan**
   (D) **Hatteras**

10. The lighter-skinned Indians had names that sounded—
    (A) **Spanish**
    (B) **English**
    (C) **Italian**
    (D) **German**

UNIT 24
A Wet, Wild Wedding

The playful dolphin known as *Tursiops truncatus*, the bottlenosed porpoise, has long been the star attraction at aquariums and oceanariums, both in the United States and abroad. You have most likely seen this ocean creature with its built-in grin on television, if not in the flesh.

Yet in 1959 tame porpoises were more a rarity—particularly in Europe. One spring morning that year, a letter arrived at the Seaquarium in Miami from Cesenatico, Italy. The people there had a problem. They had a female dolphin living in the Vena Mazzarini—"a sort of a canal with a promenade—where it makes the joy of our children and . . . even of grown-up people!"

The problem was that the female dolphin felt very lonely and was visibly suffering "by lack of companionship."

Touched by this peculiar plight, the Seaquarium's director wrote a letter asking questions about species and size. Soon he received "snaps of the bride" along with information that "Lalla" weighed 396 pounds.

He wrote: "Regarding the species, we are entirely satisfied that Lalla is a *Tursiops* and would be extremely happy to meet our *Tursiops* and welcome him with open flippers."

In Miami a contest was started to select a name for Lalla's prospective bridegroom. Fifty-nine dolphin-dubbing youngsters came up with the winning name: Palooza.

After enormous trouble and staggering complications, air and sea transportation was arranged to get Palooza to Italy. There was great cheering and much flag-waving joy as Palooza and his wedding attendants rolled into Cesenatico. Posters and banners of Palooza were everywhere. Crowds from miles around jammed the banks of Lalla's canal. The ceremony was by now an important national event.

At a signal from the mayor, amid wild cheering from the crowd, Palooza slid down the "aisle"—a wet gangplank—into the canal.

Spectators tossed hundreds of flowers, including a bridal wreath, into the water. They jammed close to view the wedding. The bride and groom got along blissfully well from the start—even though, during the ceremony, six people were pushed into the canal!

1. Tame porpoises, especially in Europe, were rare in—
   (A) 1970   (B) 1949
   (C) 1959   (D) 1969

2. One morning a letter from Italy arrived at the Seaquarium in—
   (A) San Diego   (B) Houston
   (C) Los Angeles   (D) Miami

3. The female dolphin was suffering from lack of—
   (A) food   (B) companionship
   (C) water   (D) sleep

4. Lalla's statistics showed that she weighed—
   (A) 396 lbs.   (B) 9369 lbs.
   (C) 36 tons   (D) 396 tons

5. A contest was held to give the male dolphin a—
   (A) home   (B) birthday
   (C) fish   (D) name

6. Palooza was then transported to—
   (A) Florida   (B) Spain
   (C) Italy   (D) France

7. Everywhere in the town there were Palooza—
   (A) hats   (B) posters
   (C) records   (D) songs

8. The ceremony became a national—
   (A) anthem   (B) holiday
   (C) tradition   (D) event

9. Palooza slid into the canal after a signal was given by the—
   (A) treasurer   (B) president
   (C) mayor   (D) governor

10. During the ceremony, six people were pushed into—
    (A) a car   (B) the church
    (C) the ocean   (D) the canal

UNIT 25
Talking to the Animals

Beatrice Klein lives in California with three German shepherds, a Pomeranian, and two cats. She claims she can talk to them and understand their feelings.

Some years ago Klein was walking down the street when she saw a German shepherd that looked very much like a beloved former pet that had died. Suddenly, she felt that she could read the thoughts of the strange German shepherd. After trying to communicate with other animals, Klein felt that she could talk to them by forming mental pictures and transmitting them to the animals' minds. The animals, in turn, projected images back to her, she said.

Many people, of course, are very skeptical about Klein's claims—including most veterinarians. However, some people are convinced that Klein can communicate with their pets. She has found lost dogs by "talking" to them over long distances, has diagnosed illnesses, and has apparently solved animals' emotional problems.

One day a poodle was stolen from its owner's car. Klein mentally contacted the lost dog and learned that it was in a kennel, lying in a cage beside an Afghan hound. Searching several kennels, the dog's owner found her poodle exactly as Klein had described. Another pet owner was able to find her missing cat and save its life after Klein got a mental image of it lying poisoned under a porch.

Beatrice Klein claims she once communicated with a race horse named Eagle, which had an injured leg, and learned why it was unable to get well. When it could no longer run, it had been traded by its owners for another horse. In spite of skilled treatment by vets, Eagle seemed only to get worse. Klein learned that it was very upset because it had been traded to new owners. After its original owners took it back again, Eagle started to improve right away. Klein believes that animals' emotions often keep them from healing.

Although she says she can't do it, Beatrice Klein wishes she could read people's minds as well as she does those of animals!

1. Beatrice Klein lives in the state of—
   - (A) Colorado
   - (B) Canada
   - (C) California
   - (D) Arizona

2. Klein is the owner of three—
   - (A) English bulls
   - (B) German shepherds
   - (C) Pomeranians
   - (D) cats

3. She thought she could talk to animals by transmitting mental—
   - (A) pictures
   - (B) words
   - (C) letters
   - (D) songs

4. Klein claims she has found lost dogs by—
   - (A) mentally "talking" to them
   - (B) contacting their veterinarians
   - (C) placing ads in papers
   - (D) hypnotizing their owners

5. One owner's poodle was stolen from—
   - (A) the yard
   - (B) the car
   - (C) the house
   - (D) a kennel

6. Klein communicated with the dog and found it was in—
   - (A) an animal hospital
   - (B) a city dog pound
   - (C) a kennel
   - (D) a dog show

7. One cat owner found her sick pet after it had been—
   - (A) drowned
   - (B) run over
   - (C) stung
   - (D) poisoned

8. The sick cat was lying under a—
   - (A) car
   - (B) porch
   - (C) fence
   - (D) tree

9. Klein communicated with Eagle, a—
   - (A) dog
   - (B) cat
   - (C) bird
   - (D) horse

10. When Eagle was returned to its original owners, it—
    - (A) became sick
    - (B) would not eat
    - (C) improved
    - (D) broke a leg

Do you remember the iceberg that sank the unsinkable *Titanic* (Unit 21)? How large was that iceberg? How large is any iceberg? Icebergs float on the ocean, which is salt water. Are they made up of salt water, too? Just what *is* an iceberg? Think about what you know about them. Read the following paragraph:

Quite simply, an iceberg is a gigantic chunk of frozen fresh water. Glaciers are huge compact masses of snow; as a glacier slides off a land mass into the ocean, large pieces break off. These "pieces" are icebergs, and they float, following the ocean's currents, until they eventually melt and disappear. The top of an iceberg, the part above the water, may melt relatively quickly from its exposure to the sun and wind. The bottom, or underwater part, melts much more slowly, which is why you see only a small fraction (one-tenth to one-eighth) of a berg's total mass and why icebergs are so dangerous to ships. The icebergs found in the North Atlantic are often many miles or kilometers long. Some are as much as four hundred feet high. Antarctic icebergs are much larger. Whether they are found in the North or South polar regions, icebergs have another important characteristic in common—their color.

A. Exercising Your Skill

What do you know about icebergs? How would you describe them? Make two lists. In the first, list the facts you know about the size and shape of icebergs. In the second, list words you would use to describe an iceberg.

B. Expanding Your Skill

As you read in "The *Titanic*," icebergs can pose a real threat to ships. Since the *Titanic* disaster, ships have been ever more on the alert for icebergs, and the North Atlantic is regularly patrolled. Find out some facts about how iceberg patrols work. Use the following questions to help you in your research and note-taking:

When were iceberg patrols originated?
Who pays for them?
Who actually participates in these patrols?
Do the iceberg patrols run all year?

When you have finished your fact-finding and note-taking, put your facts in order by topic and make an outline. Then give your outline a title. Compare your outline with your classmates' outlines.

C. Exploring Language

Think about what you know about icebergs:

- their size and shape
- the damage they can cause
- how ships are protected from them

Now, imagine that you're a visiting writer representing a magazine and that your assignment is to develop ideas for an article about an iceberg patrol. It's the evening of the first day. You're in your cabin thinking about what's ahead. Write a journal entry setting the scene for your next months at sea. Include facts about why you are there, about why there is a need for an iceberg patrol, and about icebergs themselves.

D. Expressing Yourself

Choose one of these activities.

1. The *Titanic* was said to be unsinkable. On its maiden voyage, it was traveling at 23 knots, a speed that was likely to set a new transatlantic record. Some people believe that the captain, the crew, and even the passengers wanted very much to break that record. What if breaking a speed record hadn't mattered to them? What if, when hearing the first warning about icebergs, the captain had ordered the ship slowed? Write what might have happened. Use the following questions to help you.

   Would the *Titanic* have collided with the iceberg?
   Would the damage have been as great?
   Would the ship have sunk?
   Would rescue ships have arrived in time?
   What do you think?

2. Icebergs are made up of fresh water. In the days of sailing ships, a ship would approach a berg gently and cautiously, and then fill up the barrels with water from its pools. Find out how, in more recent years, people have discussed using this great source of abundant fresh water and how they would get an iceberg to the area where it is most needed.

3. Underwater archaeology is a growing—and fascinating—field. Find out facts about the people who make their living as underwater archaeologists and about their discoveries. Your research might uncover facts that answer such questions as these: What special training or equipment is required? Where do such people dive, and what do they look for? What deep-sea treasures from the past have been found? What becomes of these discoveries? Share your facts with your class.